Based on an original idea by Alex A.

First published in French in 2011 by Presses Aventure under the title
Le Cerveau de l'apocalypse.

© Alex A. and Les Publications Modus Vivendi Inc., 2015
All rights reserved. No part of this publication may be reproduced, stored
in a retrieval system or transmitted, in any form or by any means without
the publisher's written authorization.

Published by **Adventure Press**, an imprint of:
Les Publications Modus Vivendi Inc.
55 Jean-Talon Street West
Montreal, Quebec, Canada H2R 2W8
www.adventurepress.ca

Publisher: Marc G. Alain
Editorial Director: Marie-Eve Labelle
Author and illustrator: Alex A.
Page layout: Vicky Masse
Translator: Rhonda Mullins

Legal deposit – Bibliothèque et Archives nationales du Québec, 2015
Legal deposit – Library and Archives Canada, 2015

ISBN 978-2-89751-166-1 (PAPERBACK)

ISBN 978-2-89751-201-9 (PDF)
ISBN 978-2-89751-202-6 (EPUB)
ISBN 978-2-89751-203-3 (KINDLE)

We gratefully acknowledge the financial support of the Government
of Canada through the Canada Book Fund (CBF) for our publishing activities.

Government of Québec – Tax credit for book publishing – Administered by SODEC

Printed in Canada

THE BRAIN OF THE APOCALYPSE

WRITTEN AND ILLUSTRATED BY ALEX A.

ADVENTURE PRESS

FOR CLAUDINE

Subject: HENRY B. BELTON

Age: 36

Weight: 125 pounds

Height: 4 feet 9 inches

Status: Kidnapped

DESCRIPTION: Henry is widely considered to be the most intelligent person in the world, even though it doesn't show. His IQ is an estimated 402.

When he was 3 years old, he was admitted to Harvard in math and advanced astrophysics. He graduated six months later.

At age 6, he beat Big Blue, the chess supercomputer.

Unfortunately, Big Blue took the defeat so hard that it decided to lead an army of robots into a war against humankind. (For details, see "The Robot War," case No. 444).

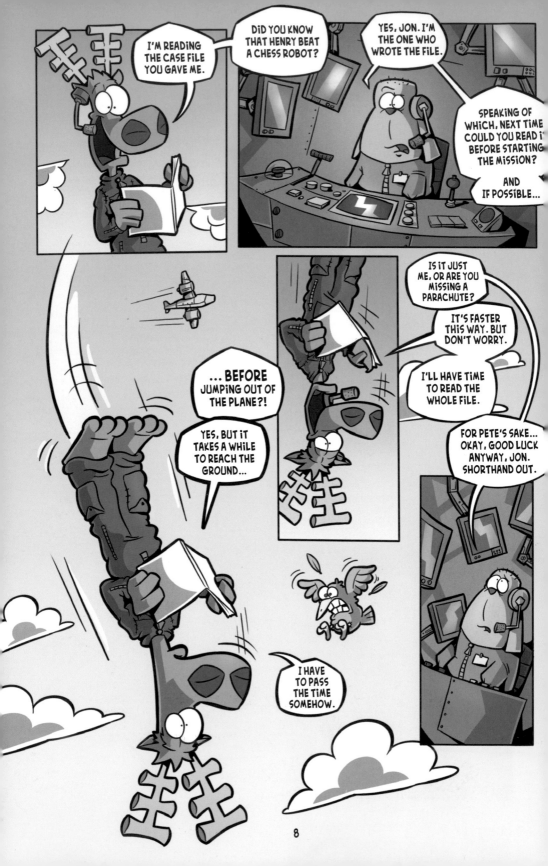

8

11

12

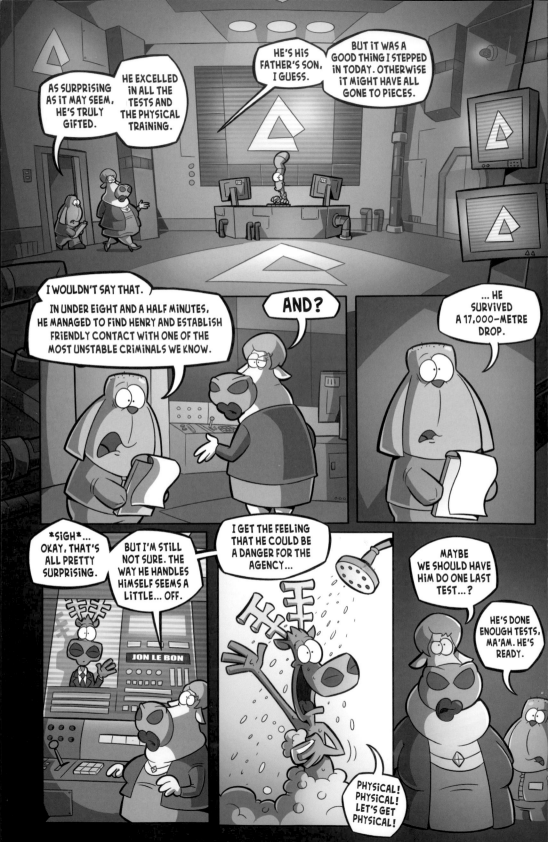

20

21

22

23

24

25

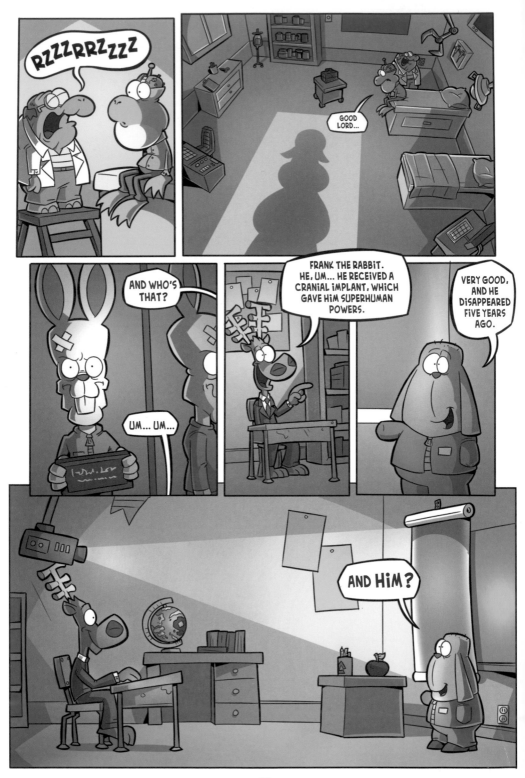

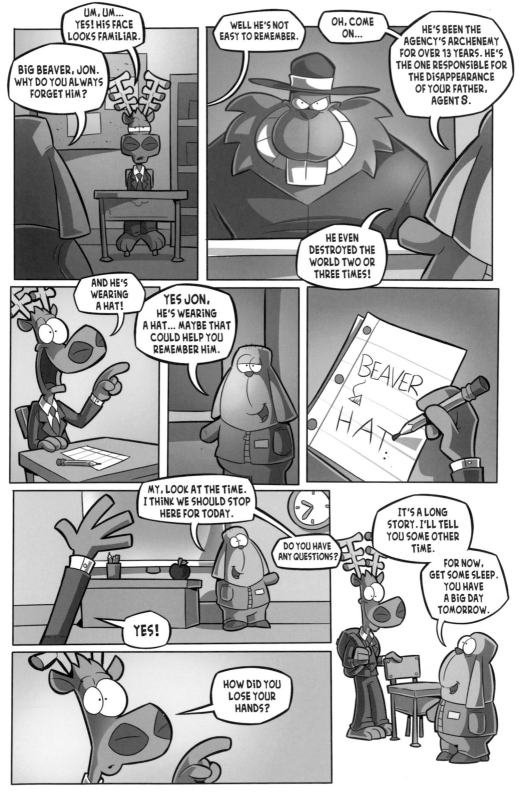

A FEW HOURS LATER...

31

32

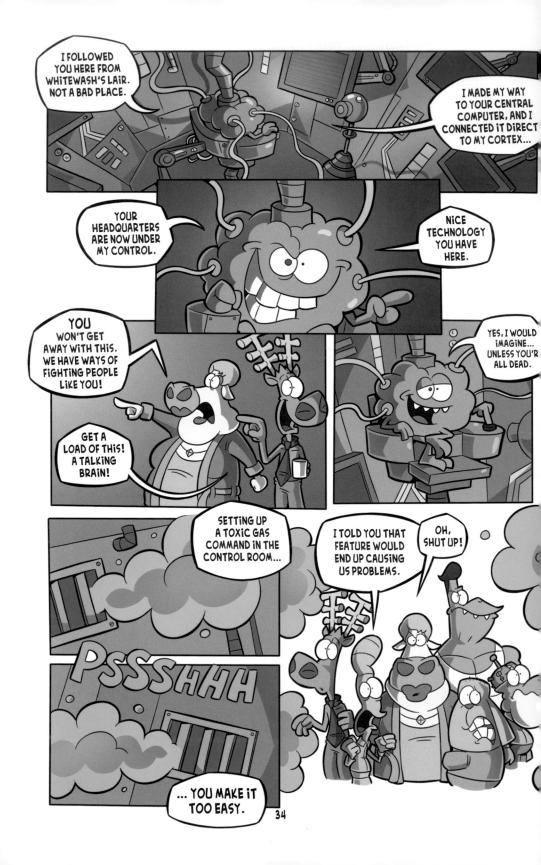

34

35

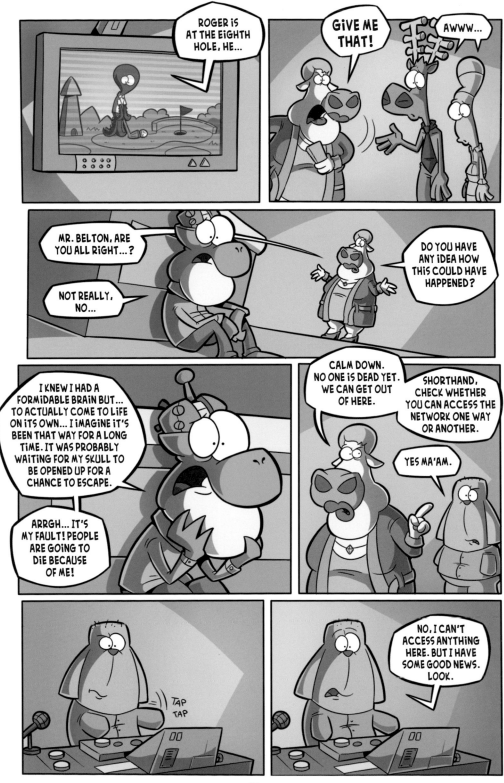

37

41

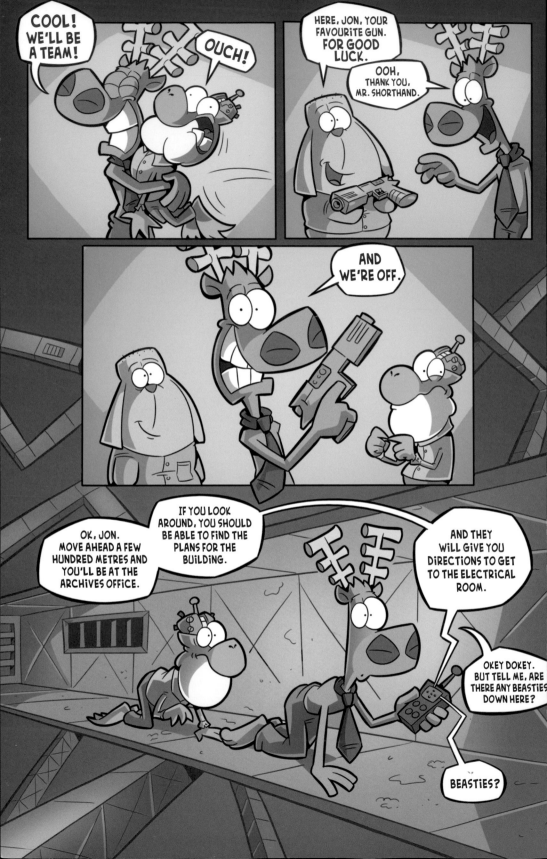

43

44

45

46

47

48

50

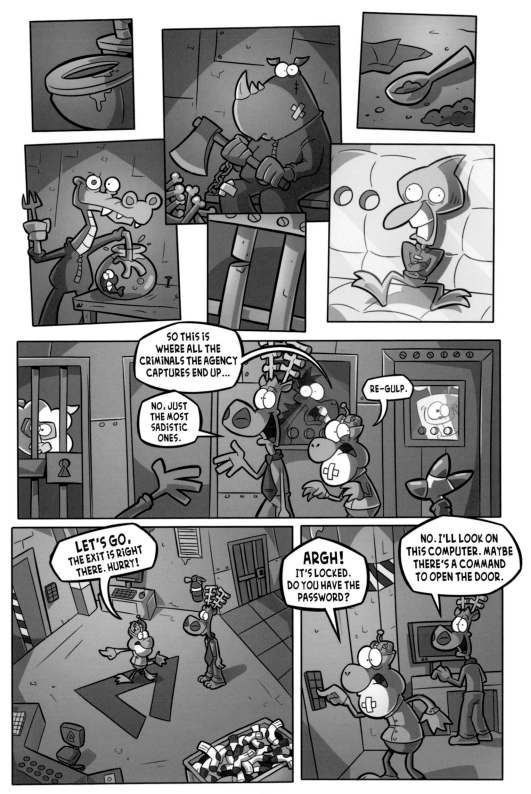

52

53

57

58

60

61

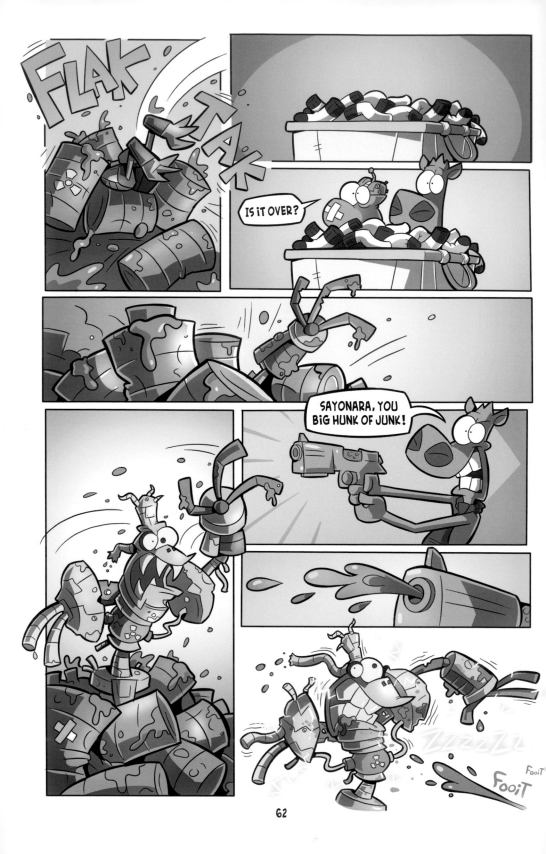

62

66

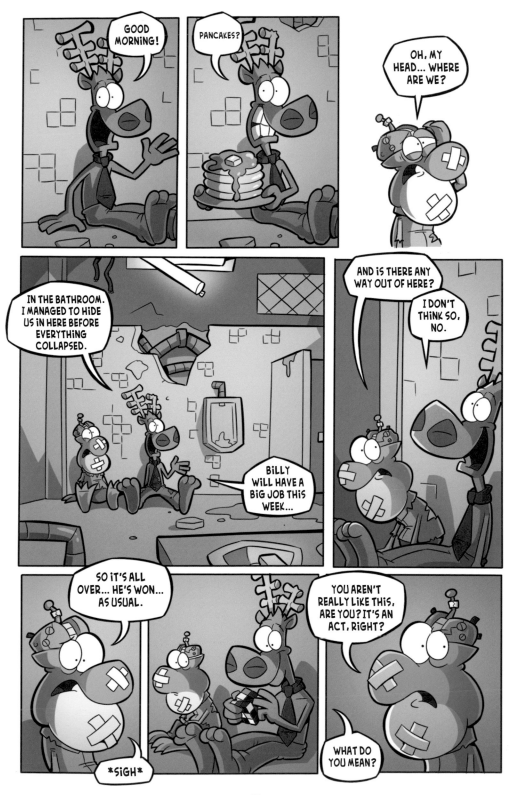

70

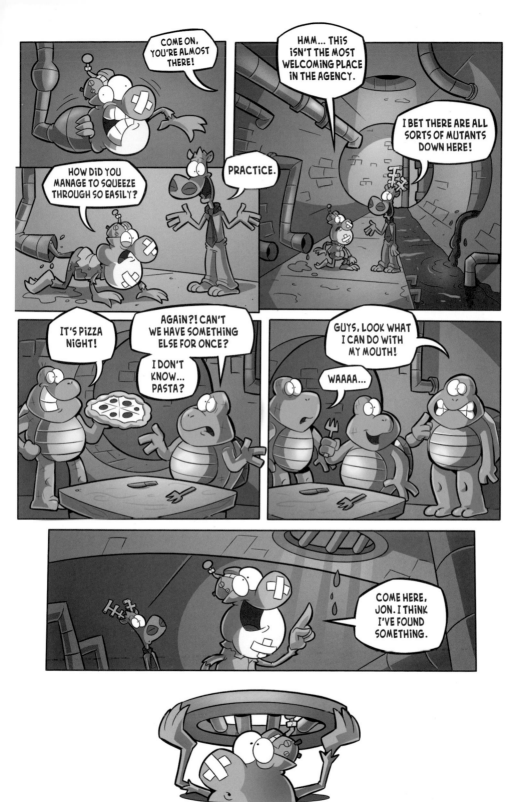

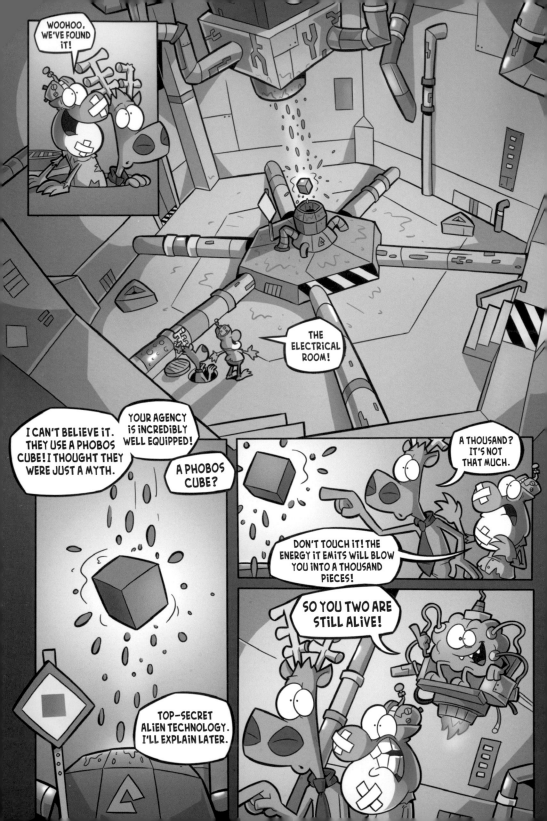

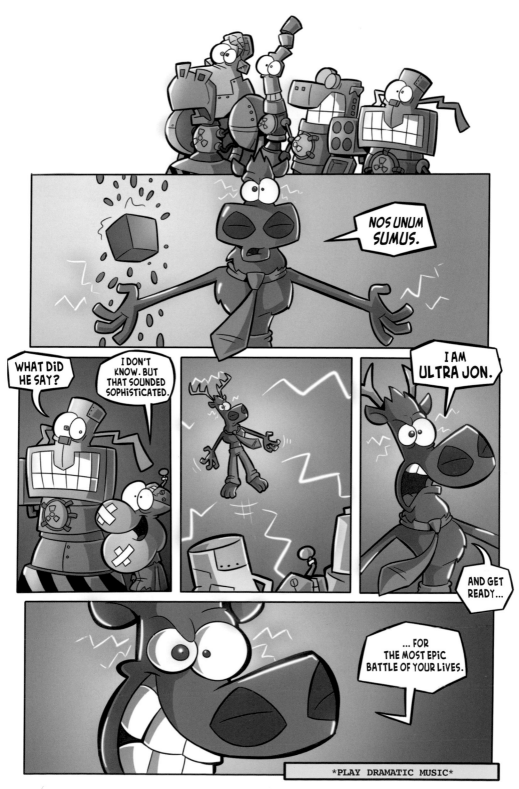

80

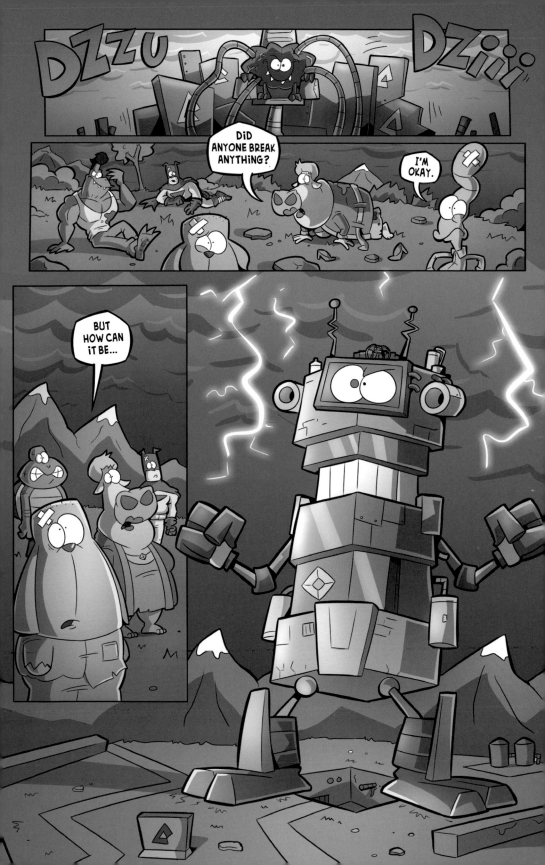

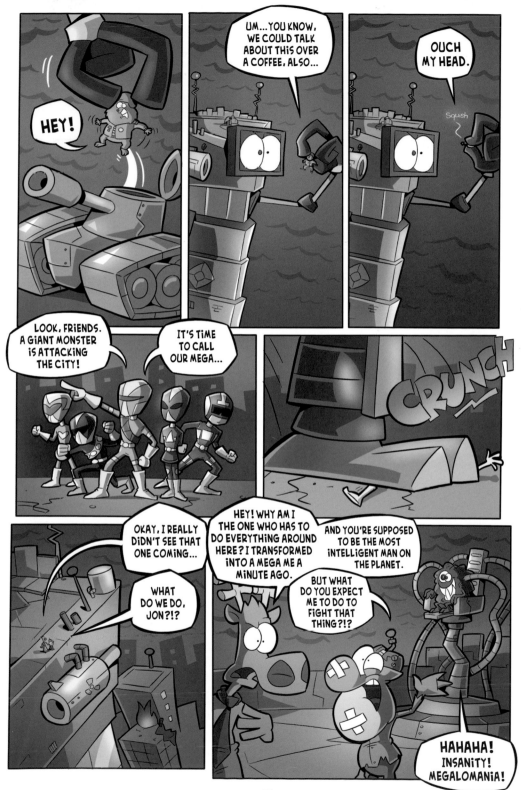

85

86

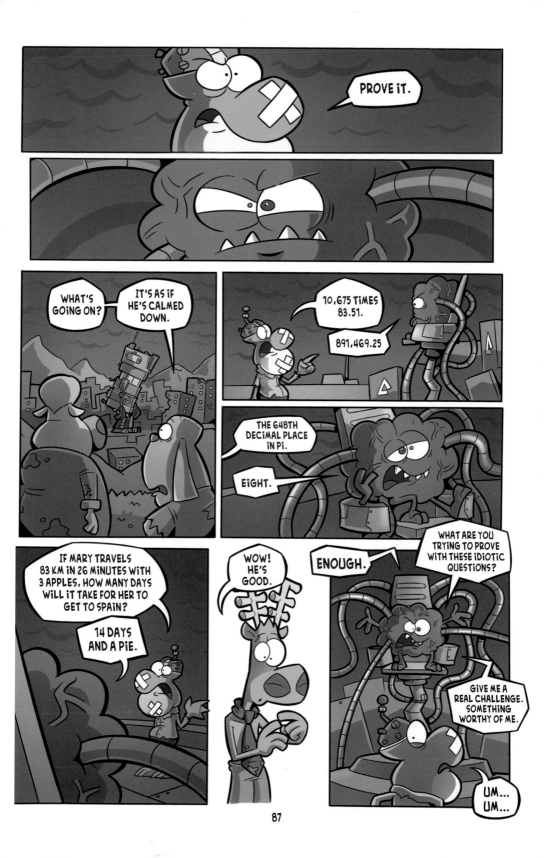

87

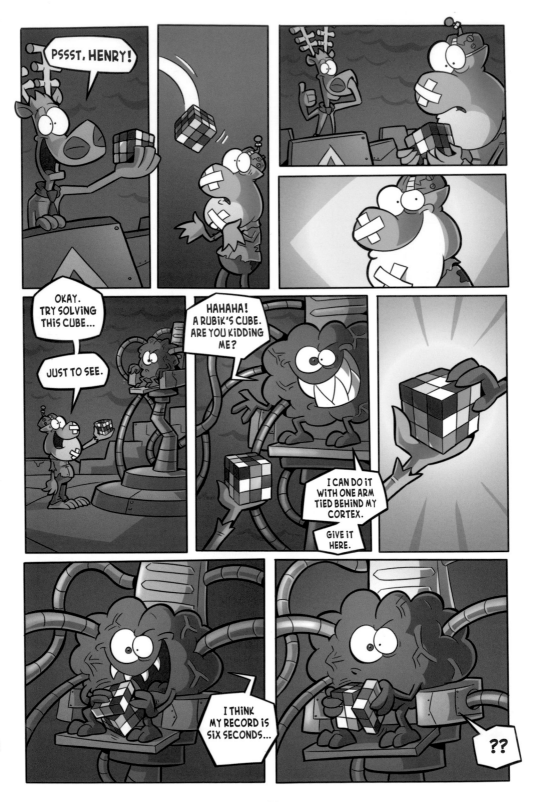

88

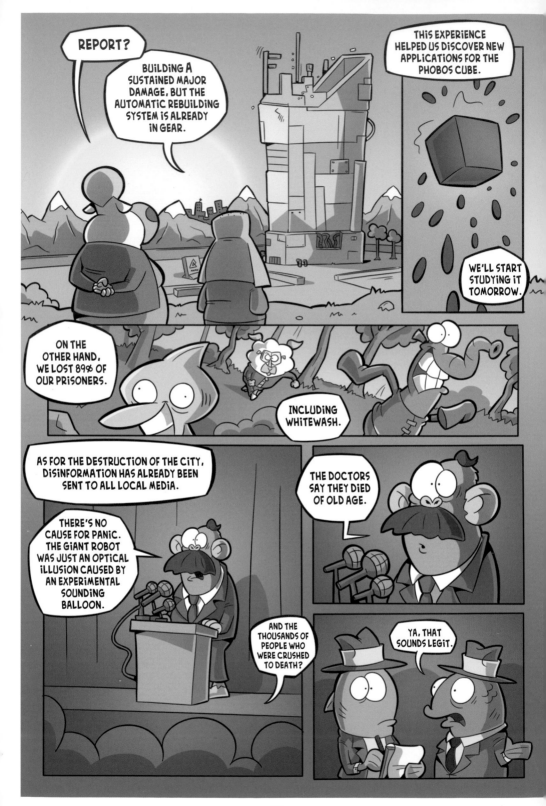

94

AGENCY ARCHIVES

Jon Le Bon's character was created a long time ago, in around 1999 (I was 11 at the time). At first, he was called Jon Bon (which sounds like "ham" in French — jambon — but word games can get old pretty fast...), Agent triple zero. It sounded pretty good but as the years went by, I wanted to get further away from other famous spies and create my own universe. This was when I started dreaming up other endearing characters to evolve around Jon Le Bon. Here now is the evolution of different characters in the series through the stages of my life.

SUPER AGENT JON LE BON

First appeared: 1999
(maybe even 1997; historians can't agree)

1999

2000

2002

2003

2005

2007

MISS MARTHA
First appeared: 2000

At first, she was just called "Mooh," but one day I realized that she needed a real name. In my mind she was head of the agency and over-seeing Jon's development as a secret agent and his overall missions to keep the World safe.

MR. SHORTHAND
First appeared: 2002

I have no idea where this character comes from… All I remember is that, basically, he was supposed to have his hands behind his back all the time. But then I realized it would be funnier if I gave him stumps and the name basically chose itself…

AGENT WXT
First appeared: 2002

I created this character in art class at age 15 I think… I was looking for new characters for my series, so I was drawing different animals in suits… and this lizard appeared, and I liked it. When I was trying to come up with a name for him, I had written several letters I thought were cool on a piece of paper to see what I could do with them. If I remember correctly, they were Y, V, W, X, T, R, K, Z. The friend who was sitting beside me said, "WXT, that's what it should be!" and I agreed. If only life was always that simple…

BILLY

First appeared: 1999

Ah, Billy… I don't remember where he comes from. I probably just needed a secretary for the Agency. Or maybe I just like drawing worms. Either way, I really like him. And he'll probably end up being a good friend of Jon's.

BIG BEAVER

First appeared: 1999

Big Beaver is practically as old as Jon himself. Logically, Jon needed the customary archenemy, and this character came to me spontaneously. My first story was a parody called *The Beaver with the Golden Gun*, inspired by James Bond's *The Man with the Golden Gun*.

FRANK THE RABBIT

First appeared: 2002

Another character that I created when I was 15 years. But unfortunately, I was never able to bestow a personality unto him. He was as boring as he looks… so I got rid of him. He made his last appearance in 2006. The reference to him in the book is accurate. Will he make a comeback some day? Probably not… If you want to see him again, start a petition and we'll see!

Alex A. is both author and illustrator of Super Agent Jon Le Bon. He discovered his love for drawing and creating cartoon characters at the early age of eight and has been at it ever since. His limitless imagination allows him to create new plots and twists and even completely new universes for his wacky and offbeat characters to evolve.

He'll tell you that his main source of inspiration is "all that exists but especially all that doesn't exist but lives in my imagination."

He's been successful as a freelance illustrator for books and magazines but his drive and determination has gotten him where he really wants to be – developing and drawing his own series.

The creation of Jon Le Bon is the culmination of many years of work, and gives us a series that is both very unique, intriguing and totally hilarious. Jon Le Bon, because of his innocence and fearlessness, can get himself in all sorts of trouble – but there's nothing he can't handle with a little help from his friends.

Alex A. lives in Montreal with his dog Wolfy and always shows up for book signings in his distinctive wool hat and colorful plaid pants, ready to entertain his young readers.

Follow Jon Le Bon in his
next big adventure:
FORMULA V